SKiD ROW

MW01014813

SLAVE TO THE GRIND

Management: Scott McGhee and Doc McGhee
 for McGhee Entertainment, Inc.
Edited by Kerry O'Brien, Steve Gorenberg,
 Jon Chappell and Andy Aledort
Music Engraving by W.R. Music
Production Manager: Daniel Rosenbaum
Art Direction: Kerstin Fairbend
Director of Music: Mark Phillips
Cover art by David Bierk
Photography by William Hames

ISBN: 089524-644-9

CONTENTS

CHERRY LANE MUSIC: THE PRINT COMPANY

EXECUTIVE: Michael Lefferts, President; Kathleen A. Maloney, Director of Customer Service; Rock Stamberg, Advertising and Promotion Manager; Len Handler, Creative Services Manager; Karen Carey, Division Secretary; Karen DeCrenza, Executive Secretary.

MUSIC: Mark Phillips, Director of Music; Jon Chappell, Associate Director of Music; Steve Gorenberg, Music Editor; Kerry O'Brien, Music Editor; Gordon Hallberg, Director, Music Engraving.

ART: Kerstin A. Fairbend, Art Director; Rosemary Cappa, Art Assistant.

PRODUCTION: Daniel Rosenbaum, Production Manager; James Piacentino, Production Coordinator.

MONKEY BUSINESS

Words and Music by
Dave "The Snake" Sabo and Rachel Bolan

kick-in' rhy-thm,_ of soc-ial cir-cum-ci-sion,_ I can't close the clos-et_ on a shoe-box full of_____ bones._

Ah!_____ Come on,_

uh! Ah,_ kan-ga-roo la-dy with her bour-bon in a pouch, she can't_

_ af-ford the rent-al on a bam-boo couch. Col-lect-ing back her fav-ors 'cause her well is run-nin' dry, I know_

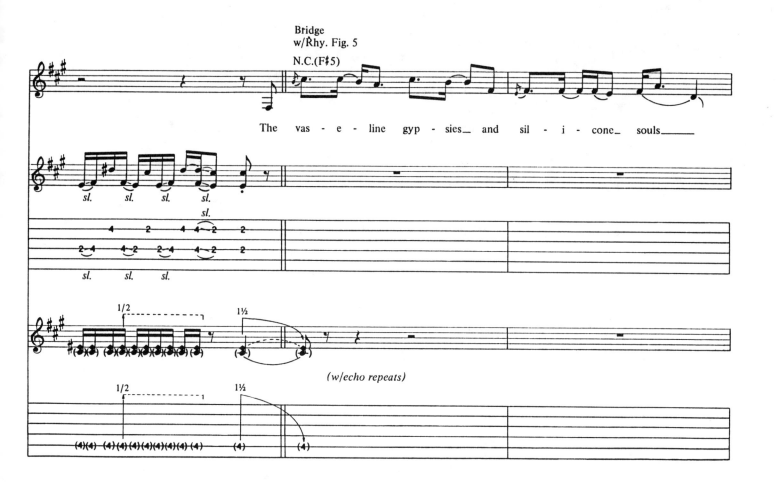

The vas - e - line gyp - sies___ and sil - i - cone___ souls_____

(w/echo repeats)

dressed to___ the so - ci - e - ty._____ The hyp - o - crite heart___ beat and___

cheap al - i - bis_____ a can't___ get___ you by___ that a mon - key._____

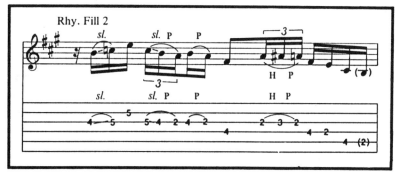

SLAVE TO THE GRIND

Words and Music by
Sebastian Bach, Rachel Bolan
and Dave "The Snake" Sabo

Bridge

swal - lowed_ their dag - gers_ by turn - ing_their trick.   They tore my_ at - ten - tion_ a - part brick_ by brick._   I'm

sick of_ the jive.   Talk ver - bal in - sec - ti - cide!_____

Guitar solo
w/Rhy. Fig. 3 (4 times)
N.C.

*Pull bar up.   A.H. pitch: C♯

Rhy. Fig. 3
Gtr. II

They

15

Lyrics under the music staves:

swal-lowed_ their dag-gers_ by turn-ing_ their trick. They tore my_ at-ten - tion_ a-part brick_ by brick._ I'm

sick of_ the jive. Talk ver-bal in - sec-ti - cide!_____

_____ Well, I won't be_ the one left_ be - hind.___ You can't be king of_ the world if you're

slave to_ the grind._ Tear down_the rat ra - cial slime. You can't be king of_ the world if you're

slave to_ the grind._ Well, I said slave to_ the grind,_ slave to_ the grind,_

slave to_ the grind!_____
(Slave to_ the grind.)_

Rhy. Fill 2

A5   G5   E5

Gtr.
II

Additional Lyrics

A routine injection, a lethal dose,
But my day in the sun ain't even close.
There's no need to waste your prayers on me.
You better mark my words 'cause I'm history. Yes, indeed.

2nd Pre-chorus:
You might beg for mercy to get by,
But I'd rather tear this thorn from my side, 'cause I... *(To Chorus)*

THE THREAT

Words and Music by
Dave "The Snake" Sabo and Rachel Bolan

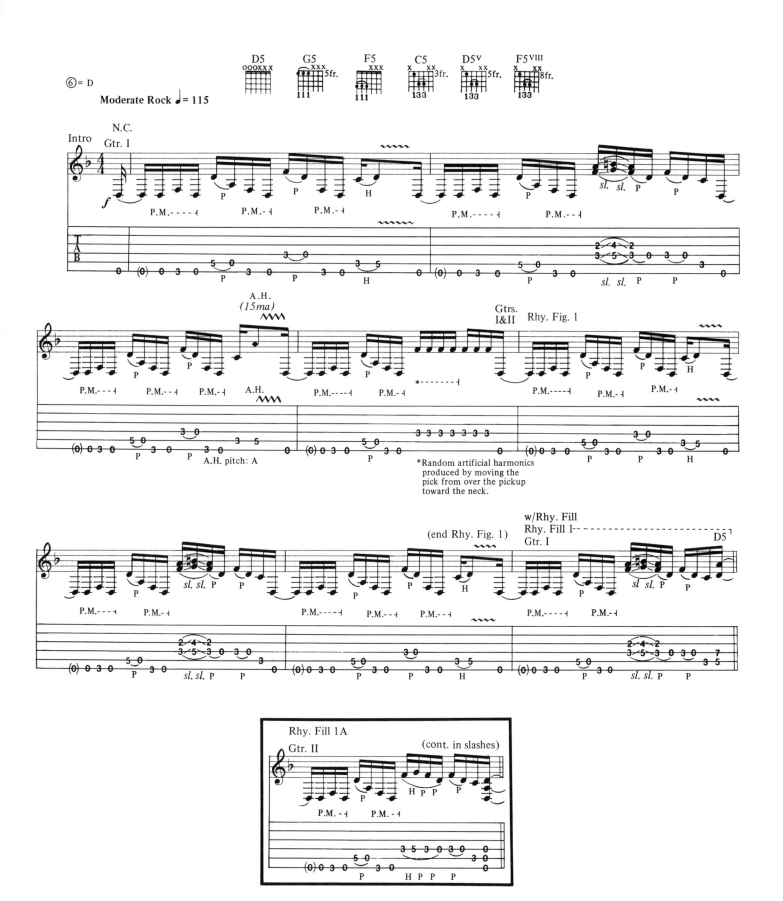

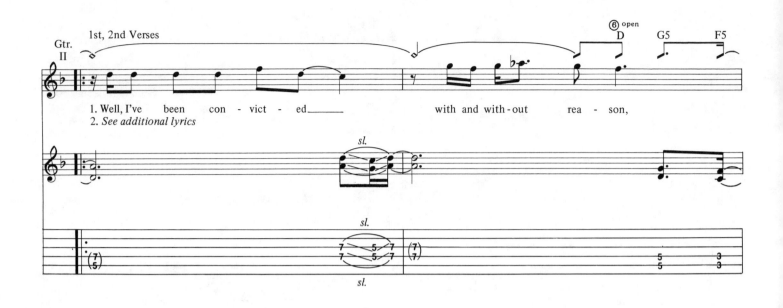

1. Well, I've been con - vict - ed_____ with and with - out rea - son,
2. *See additional lyrics*

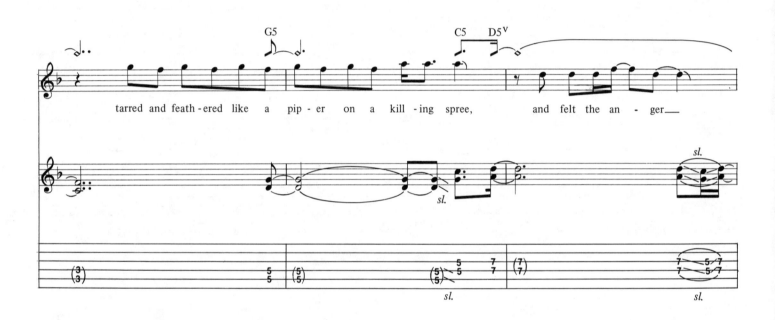

tarred and feath - ered like a pip - er on a kill - ing spree, and felt the an - ger___

(cont. in notation)

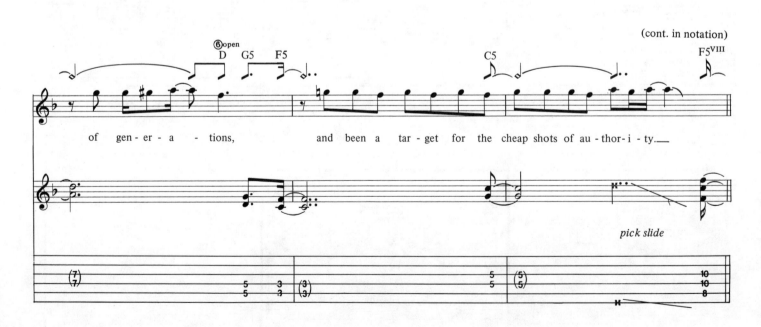

of gen - er - a - tions, and been a tar - get for the cheap shots of au - thor - i - ty.___

pick slide

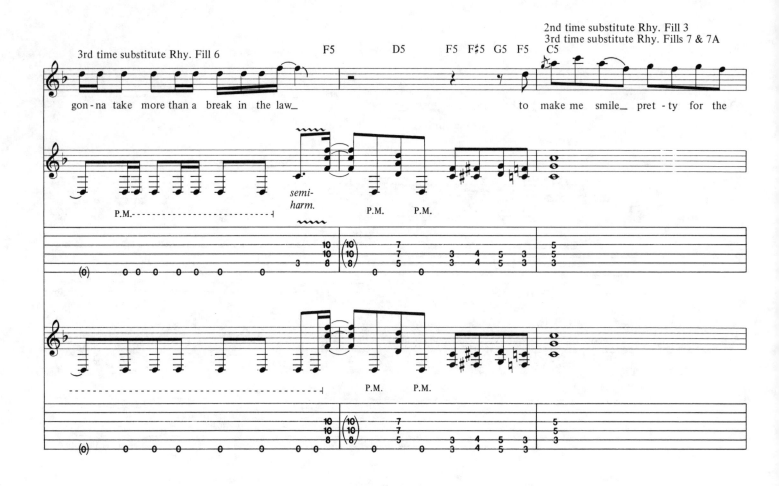

to make me smile_ pret-ty for the

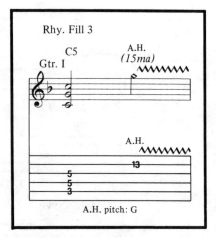

Rhy. Fill 3

Rhy. Fill 6

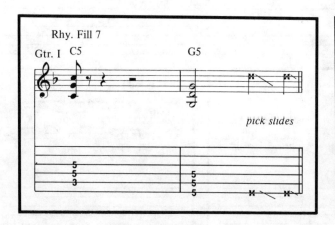

Rhy. Fill 7

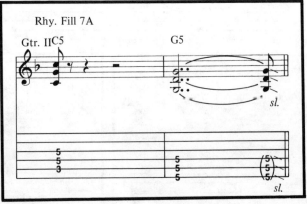

Rhy. Fill 7A

Additional Lyrics

2. I wasn't put here to be treated
   Like some disease you hoped would go away if left alone.
   Yeah, you can sweep me under the carpet,
   But I'll still infect your need to use me as a steppin' stone. *(To Pre-chorus)*

QUICKSAND JESUS

Words and Music by
Dave "The Snake" Sabo and Rachel Bolan

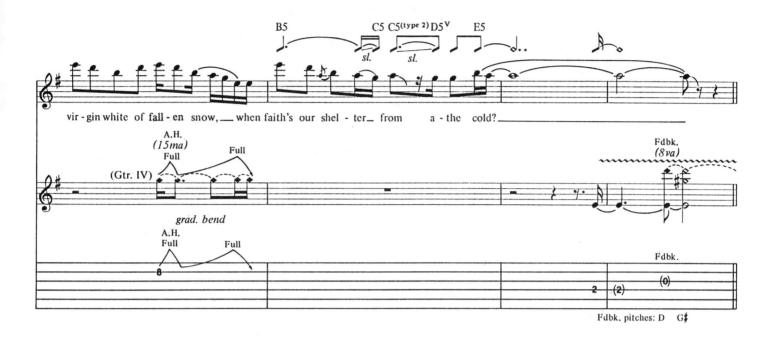

vir - gin white of fall - en snow, ___ when faith's our shel - ter ___ from   a - the cold? _____

Fdbk. pitches: D   G#

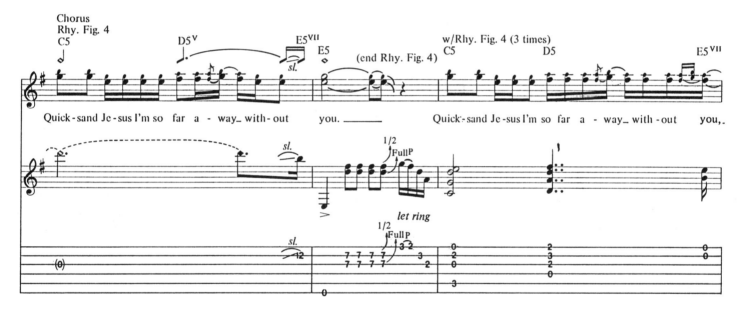

Quick - sand Je - sus I'm so far a - way ___ with - out   you. _____   Quick - sand Je - sus I'm so far a - way ___ with - out   you,.

___ oh. _____   Quick - sand ___ Je - sus, ___   I'm so far a - way,   a - way, _____ uh.

*Spring noise.

Additional Lyrics

2. A maze of tangled grace, the symptoms of 'for real' are
   Crumbling from embrace, but still we chase.
   The shadows of belief and new religion clouds our
   Visions of the roots of our souls.

   Are we ashamed of our own fate?
   Or play fool for our own sake.
   Tell me who's behind the rain.

PSYCHO LOVE

Words and Music by
Rachel Bolan

1. Check out Clem-en-tine clean-in' needles in her wine.
2. See additional lyrics

You're face down in a one-eyed world,— with a brain-dead val-en - tine.—

She'll be your zom - bie,— your liv-in' dead.— Her sweet cor-rup - tion,—

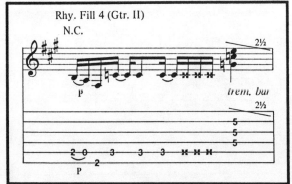

Additional Lyrics

2. Legs at ten and two,
   Chain her down, that's what you do.
   King Tut and a snake-eyed slut,
   In the pink but screamin' blue.
   I'll taste your crazy, you smell insane.
   I'm just another ghost inside your spirits hall of fame. *(To Chorus)*

GET THE FUCK OUT

Words and Music by
Dave "The Snake" Sabo and Rachel Bolan

Additional Lyrics

2. Well I puke, I stink. Bitch, get me a drink
'Cause I'm payin' for the room.
I ain't gonna buy you breakfast, so keep your mouth busy
And wrap your lips all around my attitude.
Take a walk with me with your triple double D's
And your forty foot do.
Why you walkin' funny? You must have spent some time
With the boys in the crew. *(To Chorus)*

LIVIN' ON A CHAIN GANG

Words and Music by
Dave "The Snake" Sabo and Rachel Bolan

Additional Lyrics

2. A con man's intuition can wash your sins away.
   Send your contribution, and he'll save your soul today.
   What can he know, has he been through hell and back?
   He takes the cash and drives it home in a brand-new Cadillac.

   (2nd Pre-chorus:)
   Spitting at the guard dog,
   Burning in his wicked deal.
   Screamin' down the railroad
   With no one at the wheel. *(To Chorus)*

CREEPSHOW

Words and Music by
Rob Affuso, Rachel Bolan
and Scotti Hill

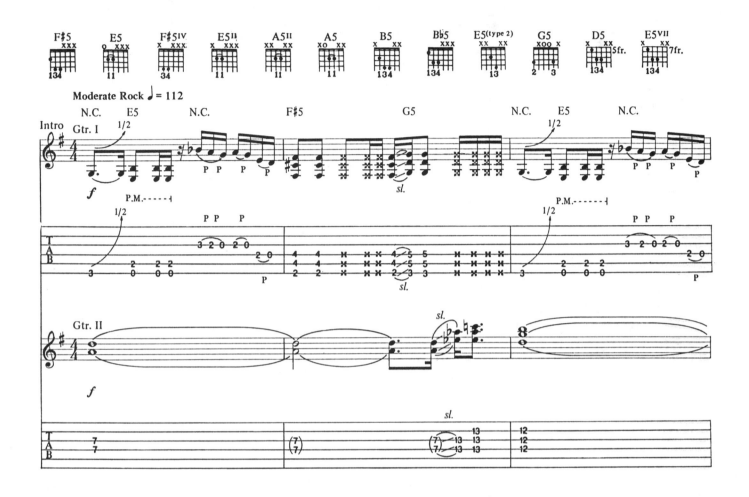

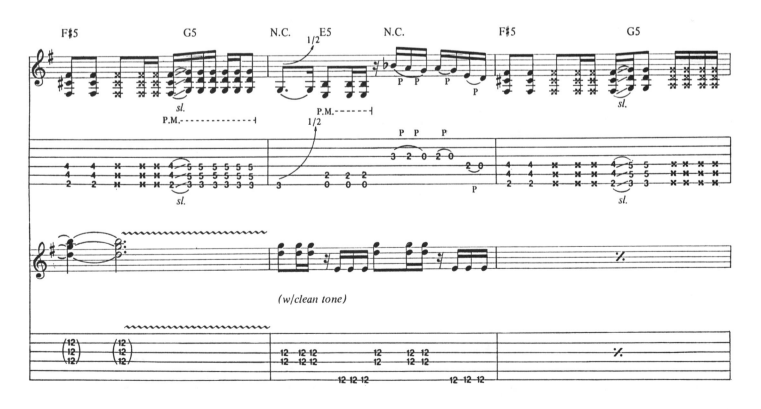

I said, I caught my wom-an on the creep-show. Hit me with a shov-el 'cause I can't be-lieve that I

(Oh, no.)

dug___ you.___

2. She dug you.___

No.___

(end Rhy. Fig. 4)

w/Rhy. Figs. 4 & 4A (3 times)

Rhy. Fig. 4 (Gtr. I)

A.H. (8va)

A.H. pitch: D♯

Rhy. Fig. 4A (Gtr. II)

(end Rhy. Fig. 4A)

(w/clean tone)

IN A DARKENED ROOM

Words and Music by
Sebastian Bach, Rachel Bolan
and Dave "The Snake" Sabo

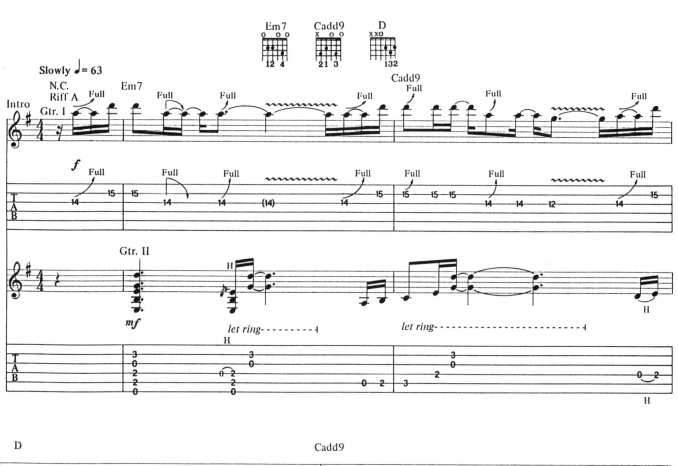

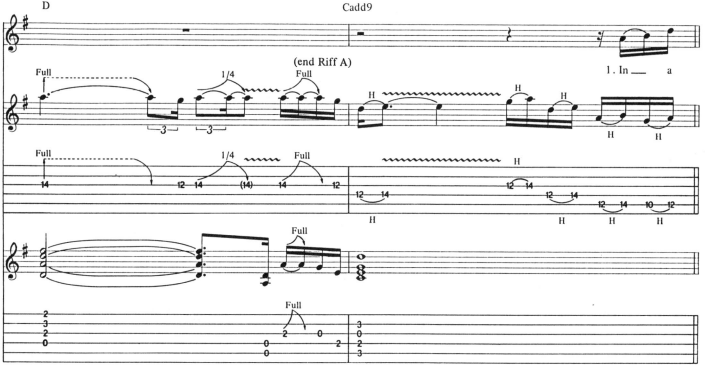

*Gtr. II plays broken chords ad lib till end.

60

2. All the precious times have been put to rest again,
   And the smile of a dawn brings tainted lust singing my requiem.
   Can I face the day when I'm tortured in my trust,
   And watch it crystalize while the salvation it crumbles to dust?

2nd Pre-chorus:
Why can't I steer the ship before it hits the storm?
I fall into the sea, but still I swim for shore. *(To Chorus)*

RIOT ACT

Words and Music by
Dave "The Snake" Sabo and Rachel Bolan

Additional Lyrics

2. I couldn't listen to a word you said.
   This goin' nowhere thing is wearing thin.
   When your sex, your drugs, and your valid vic'
   Is just the spit I wipe off my chin.
   I'd rather go nowhere
   Than not know where it's at. *(To Chorus)*

MUDKICKER

Words and Music by
Sebastian Bach, Rachel Bolan
and Scotti Hill

70

WASTED TIME

Words and Music by
Sebastian Bach, Rachel Bolan
and Dave "The Snake" Sabo

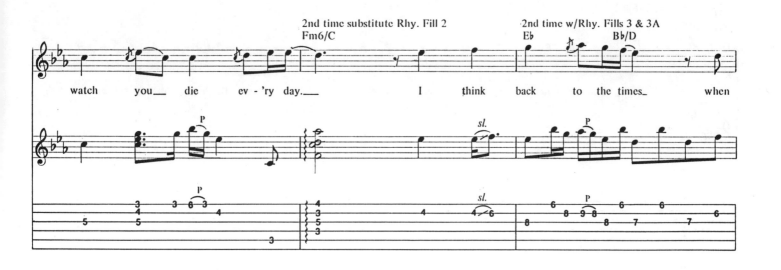

watch you___ die ev-'ry day.___ I think back to the times___ when

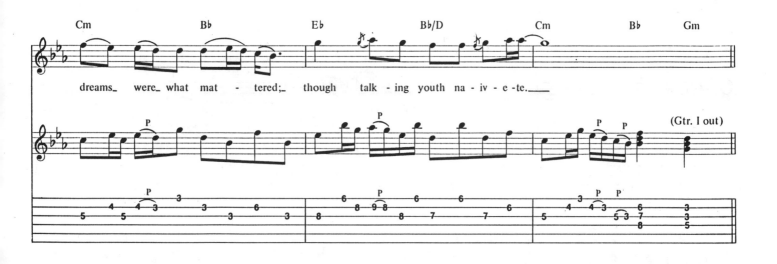

dreams___ were___ what mat - tered;___ though talk - ing youth na - iv - e -te.___

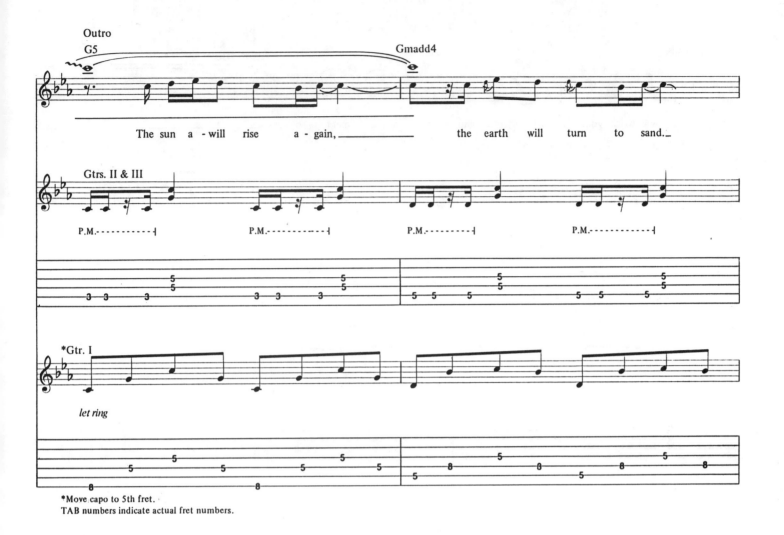

Outro

G5   Gmadd4

The sun a - will rise a - gain, _____ the earth will turn to sand._

Gtrs. II & III

P.M.----------| P.M.----------| P.M.------| P.M.----------|

*Gtr. I

let ring

*Move capo to 5th fret.
TAB numbers indicate actual fret numbers.

Eb6   Fsus4   C5

Cre - a - tion's col - ors seem to fade to_ grey.____ And you'll see the sick - ly hands of time_

P.M.-----| P.M.--------| P.M.-----| P.M.-------|

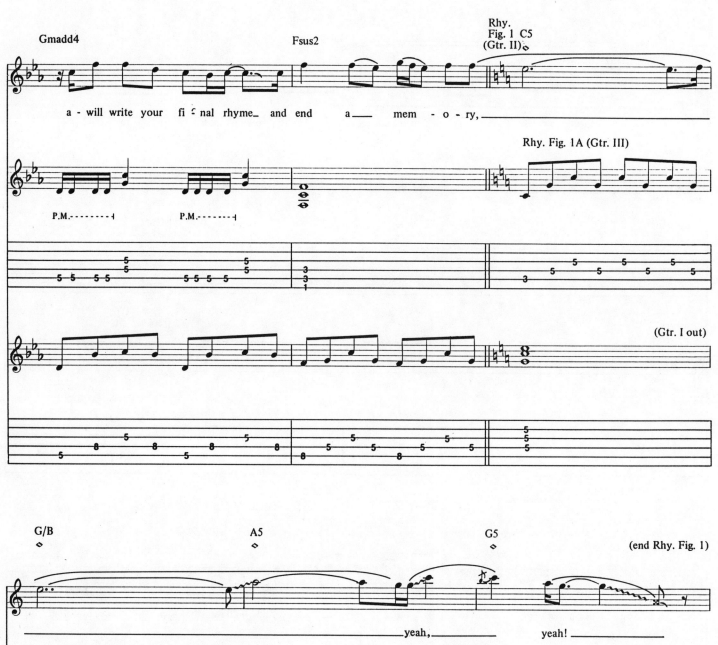

a - will write your fi-nal rhyme_ and end a_ mem - o - ry,_____

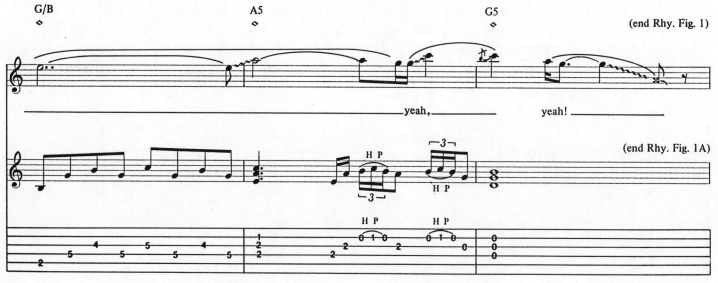

yeah,_____ yeah!_____

I nev - er thought you'd let it get_ this far,_ boy,_____

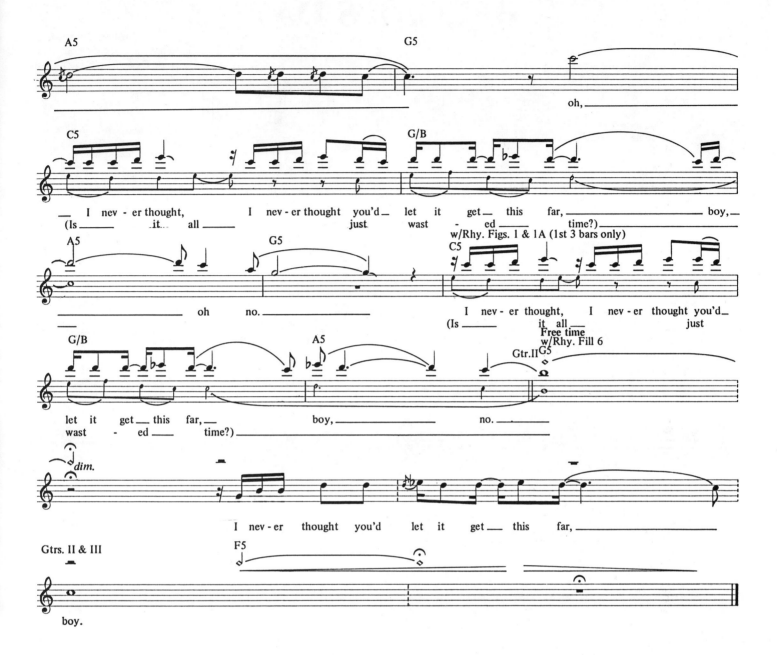

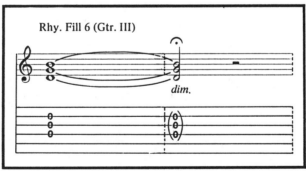

Rhy. Fill 6 (Gtr. III)

Additional Lyrics

2. Paranoid delusions, they haunt you.
   Where's my friend I used to know?
   He's all alone. He's buried deep within.
   A carcass searching for a soul.
   Can you feel me inside your heart as it's bleeding?
   Why can't you believe you can't be loved?

   2nd Pre-chorus:
   I hear you scream in agony,
   And the horse stampedes and rages
   In the name of desperation. *(To Chorus)*

BEGGAR'S DAY

Words and Music by
Sebastian Bach, Rachel Bolan
and Dave "The Snake" Sabo

be an-y ob-jec-tion or a blood-y res-ur-rec-tion? It's on-ly up to Su-zanne,

a load of am-mu-ni-tion in her hand. She had 'em

She had 'em laugh-in' in the aisles,__ Ve-nus Dee__ in the crit-i-cal file.__ She did her

Additional Lyrics

2. Oh. Adam in the chapel and he's swallowin' his apple,
Wearin' out his ball and chain.
But things were gettin' shady when the honorable maidy
Broke out the forty caliber rain.
No, no, no, no, no, no, no, no, no, no. *(To Pre-chorus)*

TABLATURE EXPLANATION

TABLATURE: A six-line staff that graphically represents the guitar fingerboard, with the top line indicating the highest sounding string (high E). By placing a number on the appropriate line, the string and fret of any note can be indicated. The number 0 represents an open string. For example:

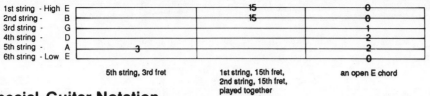

| 1st string - High E |
| 2nd string - B |
| 3rd string - G |
| 4th string - D |
| 5th string - A |
| 6th string - Low E |

5th string, 3rd fret   1st string, 15th fret, 2nd string, 15th fret, played together   an open E chord

Definitions for Special Guitar Notation

BEND: Strike the note and bend up ½ step (one fret).

BEND: Strike the note and bend up a whole step (two frets).

BEND AND RELEASE: Strike the note and bend up ½ (or whole) step, then release the bend back to the original note. All three notes are tied, only the first note is struck.

PRE-BEND: Bend the note up ½ (or whole) step, then strike it.

PRE-BEND AND RELEASE: Bend the note up ½ (or whole) step. Strike it and release the bend back to the original note.

UNISON BEND: Strike the two notes simultaneously and bend the lower note up to the pitch of the higher.

VIBRATO: The string is vibrated by rapidly bending and releasing the note with the left hand or tremolo bar.

WIDE OR EXAGGERATED VIBRATO: The pitch is varied to a greater degree by vibrating with the left hand or tremolo bar.

SLIDE: Strike the first note and then slide the same left-hand finger up or down to the second note. The second note is not struck.

SLIDE: Same as above, except the second note is struck.

SLIDE: Slide up to the note indicated from a few frets below.

SLIDE: Strike the note and slide up or down an indefinite number of frets, releasing finger pressure at the end of the slide.

HAMMER-ON: Strike the first (lower) note, then sound the higher note with another finger by fretting it without picking.

HAMMER-ON: Without picking, sound the note indicated by sharply fretting the note with a left-hand finger.

PULL-OFF: Place both fingers on the notes to be sounded. Strike the first note and without picking, pull the finger off to sound the second (lower) note.

TRILL: Very rapidly alternate between the note indicated and the small note shown in parentheses by hammering on and pulling off.

TAPPING: Hammer ("tap") the fret indicated with the right-hand index or middle finger and pull off to the note fretted by the left hand.

PICK SLIDE: The edge of the pick is rubbed down the length of the string producing a scratchy sound.

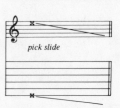

TREMOLO PICKING: The note is picked as rapidly and continuously as possible.

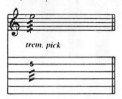

trem. pick

RAKE: Drag the pick across the strings indicated from low to high with a single downward motion.

rake

ARPEGGIO: Play the notes of the chord indicated by quickly rolling them from bottom to top. '

NATURAL HARMONIC: Strike the note while the left hand lightly touches the string over the fret indicated.

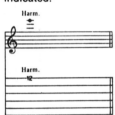

Harm.

Harm.
12

ARTIFICIAL HARMONIC: The note is fretted normally and a harmonic is produced by adding the edge of the thumb or the tip of the index finger of the right hand to the normal pick attack. High volume or distortion will allow for a greater variety of harmonics.

A.H. pitch: E

TREMOLO BAR: The pitch of the note or chord is dropped a specified number of steps then returned to the original pitch.

trem. bar
1¼

PALM MUTING: The note is partially muted by the right hand lightly touching the string(s) just before the bridge.

P.M.

MUFFLED STRINGS: A percussive sound is produced by laying the left hand across the strings without depressing them and striking them with the right hand.

RHYTHM SLASHES: Strum chords in rhythm indicated. Use chord voicings found in the fingering diagrams at the top of the first page of the transcription.

RHYTHM SLASHES (SINGLE NOTES): Single notes can be indicated in rhythm slashes. The circled number above the note name indicates which string to play. When successive notes are played on the same string, only the fret numbers are given.

NOTE: Tablature numbers in parentheses mean:

1. The note is being sustained over a barline (note in standard notation is tied), or

2. The note is sustained, but a new articulation (such as a hammer-on, pull-off, slide or vibrato) begins, or

3. The note is a barely audible "ghost" note (note in standard notation is also in parentheses).

Definitions of Musical Symbols

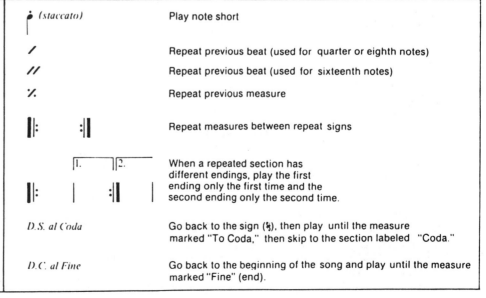

8va	Play an octave higher than written	
15ma	Play two octaves higher than written	
loco	Play as written	
pp (pianissimo)	Very soft	
p (piano)	Soft	
mp (mezzo - piano)	Moderately soft	
mf (mezzo - forte)	Moderately loud	
f (forte)	Loud	
ff (fortissimo)	Very loud	
(accent)	Accentuate note (play it louder)	
(accent)	Accentuate note with great intensity	
· (staccato)	Play note short	
/	Repeat previous beat (used for quarter or eighth notes)	
//	Repeat previous beat (used for sixteenth notes)	
%	Repeat previous measure	
‖: :‖	Repeat measures between repeat signs	
1. 2.	When a repeated section has different endings, play the first ending only the first time and the second ending only the second time.	
D.S. al Coda	Go back to the sign (%), then play until the measure marked "To Coda," then skip to the section labeled "Coda."	
D.C. al Fine	Go back to the beginning of the song and play until the measure marked "Fine" (end).	

SPEND A YEAR WITH

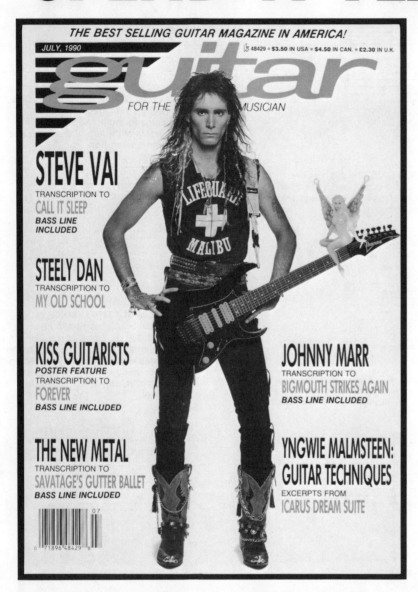
Eddie Van Halen
Steve Vai
Randy Rhoads
Yngwie Malmsteen
Jimi Hendrix
Vinnie Moore
Stevie Ray Vaughan
Guns N' Roses
Jeff Watson
Carlos Santana
Neal Schon
Eric Clapton
Jimmy Page
Jake E. Lee
Brad Gillis
George Lynch
Metallica
Keith Richards
Jeff Beck
Michael Schenker ...

AND SAVE $14.00 off the newsstand price!

Just $27.95 buys you a year's subscription to GUITAR and the chance to spend 12 months studying the techniques and the artistry of the world's best guitar performers.

Get started . . . mail the coupon below!

Every issue of GUITAR gives you:

- sheet music you can't get anywhere else — with accurate transcriptions of the original artists.

- in-depth interviews with guitar greats who candidly discuss the nuts and bolts of what they do.

- columns and articles on the music, the equipment and the techniques that are making waves.

Become a better guitarist and performer. Study with the professionals every month in GUITAR FOR THE PRACTICING MUSICIAN.

To start your subscription — *and save 33% off the cover price* — write to
GUITAR P.O. Box 53063, Boulder, CO 80322-3063